Amazing Thai Yoga Therapy for the Hands

Reusi Dottan Based Restorative and Regenerative Yoga
for
Hands, Shoulders and Heart

By
Anthony B. James

Amazing Thai Yoga Therapy for the Hands

Reusi Dottan Based Restorative and Regenerative

Yoga for Hands, Shoulders and Heart

Indigenous Traditional Thai Medicine and Yoga Therapy

By

Anthony B. James

Meta Journal Press

Amazing Thai Yoga Therapy for the Hands:
Reusi Dottan Based Restorative and Regenerative Yoga for Hands, Shoulders and Heart

By Anthony B. James

New Edition

ISBN13: 978-1-886338-15-9
ISBN 10: 1-886338-15-9

Published in USA

Inquiries should be addressed to: Anthony B. James
Meta Journal Press
5401 Saving Grace Ln. Brooksville, FL 34602 (706) 358-8646
www.ThaiMassage.Com
www.ThaiYogaCenter.Com

Printed in the U.S.A.
Cover Illustration by Anthony B. James based on photograph
        from the Sala Reusi Dat Ton, Wat Machim, Songkhla Southern Thailand
        overlaying Buddha hand from Wat Mahatat, Sukhotai.
Original art and photography by Anthony B. James. Typography by Anthony B. James.
Design art and original design by Anthony B. James.

PRINTED IN THE U.S.A. BY CreateSpace

Please note: It is important to state clearly that this body of work refers to and is a representation of a cultural heritage of the Thai nation and people. I recognize the unique and valuable body of science and information contained in the heritage of the Indigenous Traditional Thai Yoga, Ayurveda Medicine, Religious Therapeutics & Reusi Dottan CulturalHeritage to be the Indigenous cultural heritage of Thailand and the Thai people. In every way I seek to show my respect and admiration sincerely. All information, methods, traditional practices and references in this book are presented for the purpose of bringing public interest and or awareness as well as educating the public as to the value and benefit of these traditions. The Indigenous Thai Traditional Medicine practices should be recognized as one of the world's great medical heritages, bridging the gap between Classical Ayurveda, Traditional Chinese Medicine and modern western medicine.

INDEX

OPTIONAL TECHNIQUES

FORWARD: SomaVeda® Thai Hand Yoga. Reusi Dottan

The Reusi Dottan/ self Yoga techniques are not unique to Thailand in origin. Originating in both classical Indian origin reference in Vedic text such as the Jogapradipaka of Jayatarama from 1737AD, Tibetan and Chinese literature and systems. The techniques in this manual have been passed down through generations for over four hundred years. In China lore of the Wing Chun clans, legend has it that Buddhist monks and nuns, living in caves with no heat, practiced this series of postures as a system of religious therapeutics and to keep warm! In the 1600's, a teacher and former monk named Bak Mei, also called White Eyebrow, passed the practice on to his daughter, Yim Wing Chun and her friend Mai Pa Fun in what is now Fukien Province, China. These two Buddhist nuns passed the practice on to their students. Around the 1930's, the practice surfaced under a teacher named Yip Kai Man. In the 1950's, Yip Kai Man moved to Hong Kong where he taught the practice to many people, including Sifu Bruce Lee, Sifu Moy Vat and Sifu Jason Lau amd Sifu Francis Fong. I was taught the fundamentals of these exercises by both Sifus Fong and Lau in 1975.

I then practiced and refined the exercises while living and training in Thailand, adding to the repertoire of *Reusi Dottan* Reishi Yoga Asana variations found in the Buddhai Sawan Kabri-Kabrong Institute of Nongkam and Ayudthaya Thailand (Thai Martial Arts) as practiced by the Grand Master, Phaa Khruu Samaii Mesamarn, Thai Theravada monks and Reishi (Reusi) Yogis. I was honored to graduate as one of the first western Khruu's or Teachers in the Buddhai Sawan in 1984. Of the 108 Thai Reishi Dottan Asana I was taught by Phaa Khruu Samaii Mesamarn, I have chosen to emphasize primarily those which focus on the hands. There are more than 300 asana in total, not all of which emphasize the hands. I have taught this practice to several thousand professional and lay healers alike over the past thierty five years and the response and effects have been very positive. We have used these simple exercises as an adjunct in corporate wellness programs, to assist in Workmen's Compensation and disability recovery in several different industries. The results for this practice when applied to stressed individuals and those showing symptoms of repetitive stress disorders, injury and diease of the hands, elbow, arm and shoulder.

Wrist and Hand:	Elbow:	Shoulder Girdle:
Carpal Tunnel Syndrome	Elbow Tendinopathy (Tennis and Golf Elbow)	Frozen Shoulder
Strains & Sprains	Medial Epicondylitis	Winged Shoulder
Wrist Tendonitis	Flexor Tendinitis	Rotator Cuff Tendonitis
Arthritis	Ulnar Neuritis	Subacromial bursitis
Repetitive Motion Disorder	Elbow (Olecranon) Bursitis	Shoulder impingement syndrome
	Cubital Tunnel Syndrome	Supraspinatus inflammation

This list is not comprehensive. Almost any disorder with an etiology of repetitive stress, inflamation, sub-optimal range of motion, nerve stress, atrophy, arthritis etc. will respond beneficially to the emphasis of SomaVeda® Hand Yoga. In many case the positive results have been nothing short of amazing. This is especially true when the Hand Yoga was part of a comprehensive therapeutic plan emphasizing Puja, Spirit, Mind and Body, Unresolved Negative Emotional Issues (NEMO's), Root inflamatory processes, Sacred Nutrition and over all Dosha Balancing (Metabolic balancing). Several individuals have been released from the hardships of disability due in great part to these classic indigenous Prana building and energy balancing exercises. They are. however, suitable for and agreeable to all active individuals who want to maintain the health and vitality of the body and the extremities of the shoulders, arms and hands as well as the related joints. In point of fact, who does not use a computer or not perform repetitive, stressful actions in their job today? We, as modern society, are every bit as dependent on the use and dexterity of our extremities as any culture before us!

These Asana or therapeutic postions are equally practiced as meditation and Prana/ Chi development. Ancient indigenous teaching in both Yogic and Taoist traditions (both found in Indigenous Reusi Dottan) specifiy the primary benifits as being spiritual and energetic. Any physical healing which manifest is incidental to the outcomes sought for inner peace. It is simply easier to meditate when experiencing less pain. The full Vinyasa or sequence of the therapeutic positions is practiced by it'self as a form of Vipassana or moving meditation. My earnest hope is to relieve pain and suffering and to give you a tool to increase the quality of life and your ability to participate in it.

About The Author

Aachan, Anthony B. James DNM, ND (T), MSc, MD(AM), DOM, PhD, DPHC (h.c.), DMM, RAAP, SMOKH is a dedicated professor and teacher who has devoted his life and career to healing arts and sciences. The Martial Arts path that he began around age eleven eventually led him to a remote area of Thailand where he was accepted as an apprentice student of the famed Buddhai Sawan Institute. Dr. James became a recognized "Khruu" or teacher authorized to represent the Buddhai Sawan lineage of teachers and has been teaching Traditional Thai Healing arts and sciences since that time (1984).

Note From The Author
Over the years I have faced and overcome many serious health issues. In the 1960's I was diagnosed with a bone cancer in my jaw which I survived after three surgeries at Emory Medical Center in Atlanta, GA. In the middle 80's I was in a near fatal car crash which crushed several vertebrae and left me incapacitated for over a year… altogether from mayhem, mishap, competition injuries etc. I have accumulated over 41 broken bones and even had re-constructive surgery to my face.

All things being equal, I attribute my health and ability to remain functional to my Thai Yoga (ITTM) practice! My injuries and my concern over health issues of my immediate family members gave me a deep personal interest in healing. When conventional medicine failed to give the answers and relief needed I increasingly came to rely on what worked best for me… Indigenous, traditional, natural medicine was the answer. Indigenous, Traditional Thai Medicine and massage kept me going when nothing else could or would.

My training and education in Thailand began in the traditional schools of the Southern region (Buddhai Sawan, Ayurved Vidyali, Wat Chetuphon, Anantasuk) and eventually over the next thirty five years came to encompass many of the unique and traditional schools and master teachers. The three primary Southern traditions I trained in and eventually became recognized by, first as a Khruu or teacher and then eventually as an Aachan or professor, were the Buddhai Sawan (Phaa Khruu Samaii Mesamarn), Wat Pho (Moh Boonsorn Kitnyam, Moh Vilapong Sidtisoporn) and Anantasuk (Aachan Phaa Khruu Anantasuk, Moh Nanthipa Anantasuk) schools. All three of these schools allege their origins in the Royal Traditional Medicine of Wat Po. However, over several hundred years they developed their own culture and systematic practices specific and appropriate to their respective communities. Each of them have a distinctive emphasis and have incorporated various colloquial traditions and specific treatment strategies which might be very different from what we see in the official, standardized Wat Po/ The Institute of Thai Traditional Medicine at the Ministry of Public Health system taught today.

I was among the very first western students to be allowed to live and train in this way. I am also especially proud of my time training with Masters in the Northern provinces such as Buntautuk Northern Provincial Hospital and Foundation of Shivago Komarpai, Old Medicine Hospital (under Aachan, Sintorn Chaichagun, Aachan "John" Chongkol Settakorn, Khruu Pichest Bootum), Mama Lek Chaya (Jap Sen Nerve Touch), Aachan Tawee (Sawankhalok School for Blind Massage). Additionally, I was blessed to be welcomed to train with traditional medicine people in several different Hill tribes, primarily Shan, Karen, Akha and Lisu.

In 1998, I was invited to participate and present to Prime Minister Thaksin Shinawatra's "Task Force For Traditional Medicine in Thailand" in conjunction with Royal Thai Department of Commerce: Export Promotion.

On September 27th, 2002, at the Queen Sirkit Convention Center, Bangkok, Thailand I received the prestigious "Friend of Thailand" award. The award, a beautiful Ginari (Thai Angel) carved in Lucite was given in recognition of my work and contributions in the field of Traditional Thai Medicine and Thai Yoga Therapy. Accomplishments cited at the time included: publishing the first book on the Royal style of Thai Medical Massage by a US author "Nuat Thai, Traditional Thai Medical Massage" Metta Journal Press, Atlanta, GA: 1984. Becoming the first licensed Traditional Thai Massage practitioner in the United States (Dekalb County, GA 1984), the first professionally recognized Indigenous, Traditional Thai Massage Instructor in the US, American Oriental Body Work Therapy Association (AOBTA 1990 Member #37), where I also served on the AOBTA Board. Founder and President of ITTA, the International Thai Therapists Association (1992-2012, now defunct), Organizer and leader of "The Thailand Externship Training Program for non-thai practitioners" 1986 to present.

Contribution and consultation to Prime Minister Thaksins "Task Force For Traditional Medicine in Thailand" (1998-2001), Traditional Thai Massage consultant Thai Consulate USA (1998 to present). And in 2002 I was Founder, Director and Chief Instructor of a 3000 hr. professional, full time, training and certification program based on Traditional Thai Yoga medicine at that time located in Chicago.

The award was presented on behalf of Prime Minister Thaksins given jointly by the Royal Thai Tourism Authority of Thailand (TAT, now TOT), Royal Thai Ministry of Commerce: Department of Export Promotion and the Royal Thai Ministry of Health: Department of Thai Traditional Medicine, for promotion of Thai Culture and Tourism in Thailand. Over 2000 dignitaries and representatives of Thai Govt and industry were in attendance at the award.

The award itself was presented by Mrs. Juthamas Siriwan, Governor General, Tourism Authority of Thailand.

This award notes the first such formal international recognition by the Royal Thai Govt for Traditional Thai medicine and Thai Massage for a Non-Thai Instructor and practitioner. It also was the first award of it's kind for a professional organization (ITTA) representing Traditional Thai Massage in the west.

Eventually, I became affiliated with and adjunct faculty of the Anantasuk School of Traditional Thai Medicine at the Wiangklaikangwan Industrial College in Hua Hin. These programs in Hua Hin operate in conjunction with and under patronage of the Royal Thai family and King Phumipon's (H.M. King Bhumibol Adulyadej) Rajaprajanugrow foundation.

After studying and teaching for over 24 years, I received my "Aachan" or Professor recognition in Thai Traditional Medicine via the Wat Po Association of Schools (2006). This was about the same time I was assisting to develop a standardized, bilingual, Indigenous Thai Yoga and Traditional Thai Massage program under direction and patronage of Mr. Khwankeo Vajradaya, Chairman Rajaprajanugroh Foundation, Chairman Distance Learning Foundation Thailand and Grand Chamberlain to H.M. King Bhumibol.

We co-developed a program of instruction that was broadcast to over 163 vocational schools across Thailand as part of the Thai Traditional Medicine Multi-media curriculum.

In 2009 I was privileged to receive professor recognition in the Royal/Southern style of Traditional Thai Medicine and Traditional Thai Massage (ITTM/ TTM). I was issued a lifetime registry as a Doctor and teacher of Thai Traditional Medicine from the Union of Thai Traditional Medicine Society (UTTS Lifetime recognition and Teachers credentials #520121896). Additionally I was Awarded the Golden Hanneman Medallion by Doctor Aram Amradit, President and founder of the UTTS.

Throughout Asia, Southeast Asia, South America and Caribbean I traveled and lived extensively completing advanced training programs in several different countries i.e. Thailand, Philippines, Indonesia, India and China, Mexico, Ecuador, West Indies etc. My primary focus, however, is and always has been on the indigenous, traditional healing arts of Thailand.

I am proud to have received several significant formal recognitions for my teaching and practice of Indigenous Traditional Thai Medicine and Traditional Thai Massage (ITTM/ Thai Yoga).

In addition to my many years of dedicated practice of Thai healing arts and sciences, I have managed along the way to graduate with advanced medical and philosophical degrees. Two Doctoral degrees in Natural Medicine ND(T), MD (AM), Doctor of Oriental Medicine DOM, PhD (Indigenous Medicine), Doctorate in Pastoral Humanities DPHC (h.c.), RAC (Registered Ayurveda Clinician), Doctorate Classical Indian Naturopathy ND, Masters of Science Clinical Herbology MSc. and over 25 other professional certifications in various health, medical and allied medical specialties.

Currently, Dean and Director of Education for the SomaVeda College of Natural Medicine (SCNM) and Thai Yoga Center in Brooksville, Florida (www.ThaiYogaCenter.Com). The college offers 20 to 5000 hour professional development and educational programs consisting of six levels and supplemental courses. It is complimentary and designed to have parity with other similar certification training programs in indigenous, traditional, spiritually based healing arts and sciences.

My family heritage is mixed Native American/Scottish and I am proud to represent my Native American and religious heritage of practicing sacred natural medicine based on indigenous, traditional, natural principles and ceremonies. I regularly lead sacred medicine ceremonies, such as: Sacred Sweat Lodge, Sacred Pipe, Breath, and others for my community.

Although not as active in Martial Arts practice as I was in my younger days I remain an avid martial artist and hold Black Belts in several different styles and systems: Tang Soo Do Mu Duk Kwan (Master Hong Shik Chung, Lloyd Garrard), American Karate (Lloyd Garrard, Joe Corley, Bill Wallace, Joe Lewis), and Go Budo Jujitsu (Grand Master Daeshik Kim). I have enjoyed advanced teaching/instructor credentials in several types of traditional oriental arts which do not use conventional ranking such as: Jeet Kune Do (Sifu Danny Inosanto, Larry Hartsell, Alfonso Tamez), Wing Chun Kung Fu (Sifu Francis Fong, Sifu Jason Lau), Kabri Kabrong (Grand Master Samaii Mesamarn), Zhang Yuan Ming Chi-Gung (Master Zhang Yuan Ming) and the Filipino arts of Kali (Sifu Danny Inosanto), Pekiti Tirsia (Tuhon Leo T. Gaje Jr.), Arnis de Mano (Jorge Lastra), Armas de Mano (Dionisio Canete, Nick Serrada) and Indonesian Pencak Silat (Pendekar Suyadi Jaffri: Jakarta).

I hold the office of Knight Chevalier/Grand Council Member and volunteer as a Diplomat with the UN DESA NGO Sacred Medical Order of the Knights and Church of Hope (SMOKH/ SMOCH), a Diocese of the Eastern Orthodox Catholic Church and Grand Priory of the Hospitaller Knights of St. Lazarus of Jerusalem (HOSLJ) doing volunteer work on medical missions in Ecuador, West Indies and other countries. SMOKH gives me the opportunity to practice natural medicine in and with indigenous communities and the Thai work is always well received and respected. I am also an ordained priest in both the SMOKH Diocese under protection of the Eastern Orthodox Catholic Church and am a Director of the Priory of Saving Grace Church: SMOCH Priory #110 located in Brooksville, Florida.

THAILAND is situated in the southeast part of Asia between 5 degrees north parallel, and 21 degrees north parallel, 97 degrees east latitude and 106 degrees longitude. It is bordered by the countries of Myanmar (Burma), Kampuchea (Cambodia), Laos and Malaysia. The terrain is quite diverse with sub-tropical lowlands bordered by the gulf of Siam in the south, the spacious great central plains of Menam Chao Phraya, and the craggy mountains of the Northern Highlands.

Note how centrally located in South and S.E. Asia the country of Thailand is. Not far geographically from India, China and the Philippines by land, river or ocean.

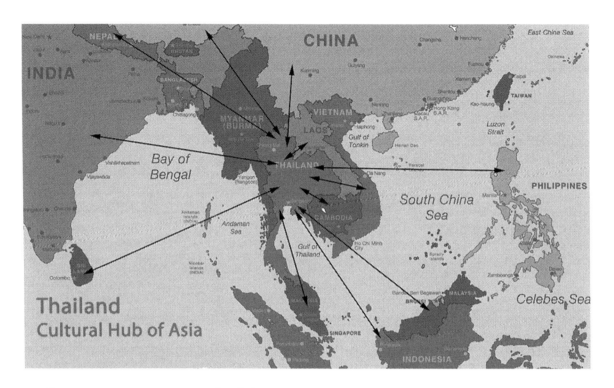

Notice in this French map circa 1700 the varied and diverse cultural world Siam co-existed with at that time.

History of Ayurveda and Reishi Yoga in Thailand:
Origins of Indigenous Traditional Thai Medicine and Massage

Indigenous, Traditional Thai Massage (Indigenous Thai Yoga Therapy), also called *"Ryksaa Thang Nuad Phaen Boran Thai"* or the "ancient Chirothesia (Yoga Therapy) or hands-on healing" of Thailand, is born of a long tradition. This unique system of indigenous, traditional, natural medicine and Yoga therapy finds it's ancient roots first in the traditions of classical Ayurveda as far back as the 5th century BCE. Subsequently the Vedic health and medical practices eventually became common practice in SE Asia, and Burma (Myanmar) and Thailand were heavily influenced by succeeding generations of Buddhist influence, philosophy and practice. Some form of this traditional medicine has been taught and practiced in various locations for about 2500 years.

When Theravada Buddhism arrives in the region (400-600 C.E.) it is firmly established as a colloquial and unique variation still founded primarily on its Vedic roots but progressively influenced by the diversity which is found in early Thailand beginning in the Sukhothai period, followed by the Ayutthaya and Bangkok eras. Beginning in the Ayutthaya period (1351) we see influences from the Burmese, Japanes, Chinese, Malay, Philipines and Portugal [3] consistent with the immigration and trade of the Kingdom during that time. This is also when we note the first documented arrival of western doctors. Traditional Burmese medicine especially came to the forefront before and after the sacking of Ayutthaya between 1765 and 1767 [4].

The classics of Indian literature and Ayurveda were known and being distributed and or used by the Royal Court in Ayutthaya such as the Ramayana, Rig Veda, Athara Veda, Pradapika and Sushruta Samhita. Additionally, the Thai Royal court from earliest days was likely knowledgeable, by way of local culture and the literature of the Vedas and the Puranas, of the Hindu deities and in particular the deity and iconic symbols associated with Dhanvantari (*Thai Pra Narai, Narayana, Jagannath*). It may be interesting to note that one of the oldest bronze statues in Thailand, now located in the National Museum in Sukhothai is that of Vishnu. Dhanvantari is an avatar of Vishnu in Hinduism. He is the physician to the Gods and generally the deity/spiritual icon of Ayurveda.

During the periods of war with neighboring Burma, many tens of thousands of Thai people were taken as prisoner and held for over 40 years before being able to establish their freedom and return to their homes, including the famous Thai Prince and later King Naresuan [5] [6]. When they returned they brought with them knowledge and practices obtained during their captivity including medicine, martial arts, music, food and more. These were incorporated into the dominant Thai culture over time and remain influential today by way of the many generations of Burmese people immigrating and now living in Thailand.

Historically, the initial credit for the origination of what becomes Indigenous, Traditional Thai Medicine and Massage is given to one individual, a famous Indian doctor called Jivaka Komalaboat [12] (*Shivago*) other spellings include Jivaka Kumar Bhaccha and Jivaka Amravana. Jivaka, of Indian origin, is alleged to have been born in what is today the city of Rajgir, the ancient capital of the Magadha Kingdom (Later Majapahit/ Bihar). There are several different accountings of his birth, life, education and teachings.

In looking for references that were more detailed and or which offered historically verifiable references to the life of Jivaka. I found several. One specific account crossed reference several other however, without specific references it is hard to verify all details. However, I am including it under fair use to present the details for further research and or verification: According to one author (Salina- Nalanda University) "According to the Anguttara commentary he was the son of Salavati, a courtesan of Rajagaha with Abhayarajakumara (Son of Raja Bimbisara) but some accounts maintain Jivaka (Shivago) was Ambapali's son with Raja Bimbisara. As per the Vinaya sources the child was placed in a basket right after birth and thrown on a dust-heap, from where he was rescued by Abhayarajakumara.

When questioned by Abhaya, people said "he was alive" (jivati), and therefore the child was called Jivaka; because he was brought up by the prince, he was called Komarabhacca (child of a Prince). It has been suggested, however, that Komarabhacca meant master of the Kaumarabhrtya science (the treatment of infants); *VT.ii.174; in Dvy. (506-18) [12]* he is called Kumarabhuta because of his medical profession.

When he grew up, he learns of his antecedents, and went to Takkasila without Abhaya's knowledge and studied medicine for seven years. When he returned to Rajgir, Abhaya established him in his own residence. There he cured Bimbisara of a troublesome fistula and received as reward all the ornaments worn by Bimbisara's five hundred wives.

DalhaSa, the 12th century commentator of the Susruta Samhita, says that Jivaka's compendium was regarded as one of the authoritative texts on the subject. Another text that quotes Jivaka's formulas is the Navan_taka (meaning 'butter'), a part of the Bower MSS discovered in 1880 from Kuchar in Chinese Turkistan. Based on earlier standard sources, this medical compilation of the 4th century AD, attributes two formulas dealing with children's disease to Jivaka, saying '*Iti hovaca Jivakah*, i.e. thus it spoke Jivaka. One formula is: i.e., Bhargi, long pepper, Paha, payasya, together with honey, may be used as linctuses against emeses due to deranged phlegm." A "Linctus" is a form of cough medicine [13].

In researching Jivaka, Rajgir and the ancient Nalanda University, there are references to Jivaka and also in connection with the Buddha from the Chinese authors Xuanzang (Hiuen Tsang) and Yijing, especially those of Xuanzang (Sixth Century between 630 and 643 CE). In one of his accounts he writes "*North-east from Srigupta's Fire-pit, and in a bend of mountain wall, was a tope (stupa) at the spot where Jivaka, the great physician, had built a hall for the Buddha. Remains of the walls and of the plants and trees within them still existed. Tathagata often stayed here. Beside the tope the ruins of Jivaka's private residence still survives.*"

Referred to in some ancient references as the Thrice Crowned King of Medicine, he was a classically trained Ayurvedic physician probably in the tradition of Atreya (Atreya Punarvasu/ Takkasila). Jivaka was known to be influenced by Buddhism and was possibly the personal physician to Raja Bimbisara, the Magadha king of that period and to the Buddha and local monks community on appointment of the king.[12] It is possible today to travel to see Jivaka's home and the ancient Nalanda University in Rajgir still today.

His name is mentioned in the traditional Pali canon or writings of Theravada (Hinayana) Buddhism (Zysk, Kenneth, G. 1982). Pali is anachronistic/ancient Sanskrit language still in use today by Theravada Buddhist monks. "Studies in Traditional Indian Medicine in the Pali Canon: Jivaka and Ayurveda", (Kenneth G. Zysk, Journal of the International Association of Buddhist Studies 5, pp. 309–13) [15]. There are numerous additional references to him, his life and healing practices in the Pali Cannon (liturature). In fact there is some support for the idea that the "Giving of Robes" (Vin.i.268-81; AA.i.216) [16] where he made a gift to the Buddha of "a celestial shawl he received from king named "Chanda Pradyotha" prompting the Buddha to give a famous sermon leading to the practice still followed today.

Another example found in the Pali Canon has Jivaka directly treating the Buddha for specific ailments using Ayurveda. "Once when the Buddha was ill, Jivaka found it necessary to administer a purge, and he had fat rubbed into the Buddha's body and gave him a handful of lotuses to smell. Jivaka was away when the purgative acted, and suddenly remembered that he had omitted to ask the Buddha to bathe in warm water to complete the cure. The Buddha read his thoughts and bathed as required. (Vin.i.279f; DhA. (ii.164f)" [17]

The above is an example of the therapeutic adjuncts we use in ITTM today: Chirothesia, Anointing, Oliation, Herbology, Aromatherapy, Pancha Karma, Marma Cichitsa etc.

During his time in association with the Buddha he became a Buddhist monk (*Sotapanna*) and continued to practice medicine and develop the strategies that would be the foundation for medical and healing practice in Buddhist temples until the present day.

Jivaka was eventually declared by the Buddha chief among his lay followers loved by the people (*aggam puggalappas-annanam*) (A.i.26)[18]. He is included in a list of good men who have been assured of the realization of deathlessness (A.iii.451; DhA.i.244, 247; J.i.116f) [19].

He seemed to follow, teach and or exemplify the doctor's moral obligations (Doctors Code of Conduct) as found in the Pali scripture, the Vejjavatapada. Attributed to actual practices and teaching directly from the Buddha. In the seven articles, excerpts from four passages in the Pali canon, the Buddha lays down the attitudes and skills which would make "one who would wait on the sick qualified to nurse the sick." (Anguttara Nikaya III, p.144) [20]. The Vejjavatapada likely predates the Greek Hippocratic Oath. It does not just exhort doctors to practice ethically, it clearly specifies a true holistic practice of medicine addressing the spirit, mind and body in an integrated fashion.

The Lord said: "Health is the greatest gain." He also said: "He who would minister to me should minister to the sick."
        I too think that health is the greatest gain and I would minister to the Buddha.
Therefore:
A) I will use my skill to restore the health of all beings with sympathy, compassion and heedfulness.
B) I will be able to prepare medicines well.
C) I know what medicine is suitable and what is not. I will not give the unsuitable, only the suitable.
D) I minister to the sick with a mind of love, not out of desire for gain.
E) I remain unmoved when I have to deal with stool, urine, vomit or spittle.
F) From time to time I will be able to instruct, inspire, enthuse, and cheer the sick with the Teaching.
G) Even if I cannot heal a patient with the proper diet, proper medicine and proper nursing I will still minister to him, out of compassion.
        Translated from Pali into English by Bhante Shravasti Dhammika

The Brahmajala Sutra says: *"If a disciple of the Buddha sees anyone who is sick, he should provide for that person's needs as if he were making an offering to the Buddha."* [12] Brahma Net Sutra, STCUSC, New York, 1998, VI,9[21]'

Jivaka is revered to this day. Many modern practitioners and schools begin every healing session with recitation of a Pali Mantra called *OM NAMO SHIVAGO*. Royal practitioners generally do this quietly while in the North of Thailand the Mantra may be recited out loud, sometimes with the receiver participating as well.

The *Wai Khruu* or paying of respect to Jivaka (Shivago) is still done partly in remembrance of his contribution to the present day art. It is impossible to say to what extent other styles of medicine and massage have contributed to Indigenous, Traditional, Thai Medicine (TTM/ ITTM) development.

The current capital of Thailand, Bangkok, was established in 1782 with the coronation of Chakri King Rama I in 1782. According to Thai historians the first meaningful building to be erected in the new capital was the rebuilding of the new Wat Pho (1789-1801). The original in the former capital (Ayutthaya) having been burned by invading Burmese armies.

Primarily ITTM has been passed from one generation to the next in the form of an oral tradition, whereby one would serve an apprenticeship under a teacher, often for several years before practicing as a practitioner. In general, the teachings were preserved and cherished by the monks and nuns of the Buddhist Temples. In addition to the oral tradition there have been several treatises, hand written papers, Codices and or books written mostly for or by the Royal Court and not easily obtained by the general public. The most accessible documents detailing the practices of the Royal Court Traditional Medicine, were the stone carvings, built into the walls and pavilions of Wat Po in Bangkok. More on these later.

Important to note also is that there have always been, from earliest days to the present, two different corollary systems of practice: Two types of traditional curing methodologies and or points of view in the way healing and traditional medicine was practiced in Thailand. The urban or variant descendant practice from the Royal schools of traditional medicine and the country/ rural and or common practices found in the

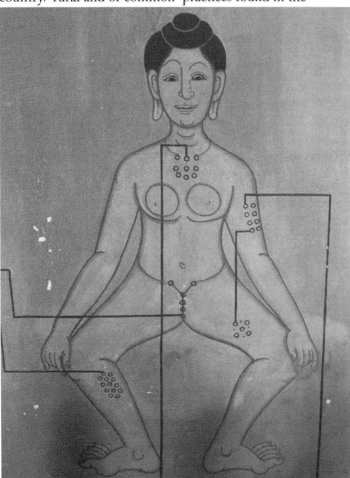

village, jungle and countryside. The urban represents efforts at standardization and training, the rural or country incorporates the more indigenous ideas and practices restricted by tribe or geographic location. Most researchers agree that there has always been and still is cross sharing of ideas, influences and practices of both systems.

Similar variations of this indigenous traditional medicine are practiced in Sri Lanka, Burma, Laos, Cambodia and, of course, Thailand. There is also a dramatic similarity to Traditional Tibetan Medicine, Amma/Tui Na of China, the Anma/Shiatsu of Japan, and Filipino Hilot.

History is unclear as to when specific developments were incorporated into the traditional medicine catalog of practices. Additionally there is a lack of documentation of the family, tribal and village specific practices that were passed on through oral tradition and not documented in the "official" and or sanctioned records and historical text. Further example is the significant differences, both historically and in contemporary, between "Official" Traditional Medicine practices and the "Rural" traditional medicine practices found in remote villages and among tribal communities.

"Chart depicting female balancing points: Wat Po Massage Pavilion"

We don't see the first official documentation until King Rama commissions the medical tablets (epigraphies) made and enshrined at the new Wat Pho in the 1830's. According to the custodians of Wat Pho, after the capital (Ayutthaya) was destroyed in 1767 by Burmese invaders, rescued fragments of the original documents were used by King Rama to make the new ones.

These tablets are a text of the theory behind ITTM and show the Sen or lines of energy running throughout the body.

These charts of stone depict sixty figures, thirty of the front and thirty of the back. There are channels and points clearly displayed. One interesting observation is apparent: many channels directly correspond to Chinese meridians and special or Extraordinary vessels. Others correspond to the concepts of Prana Nadis from classic Indian Ayurvedic medical science. The charts detail many major and minor Marma/Chakras or centers of energy. In Traditional Thai Medicine these centralized point locations of energy/wind/breath/air are called "Lom" or Wind Gates.

Wat *Raja Orasaram Ratchaworawiharn*

The depiction of the knowledge of traditional medicine at Wat Po (Bangkok) and also at Wat Raja Orasaram Ratchaworawiharn (Thonburi) were considered incomplete. This was perhaps intentional as the "Secrets" of healing practiced by the Royal Court Doctors (Maw Nuad) at that time were closely guarded. The Royal practice of medicine was more likely passed on from one generation to the next within the family... father to son or nephew in formal apprenticeship.

In addition to the famous "Epigraphies of King Rama" (Carved stone medical text) located at Wat Po and Wat Raja-Orasaram (King Rama III: in the Thai/ Chinese style called "The Royal Favorable Art" style) , there are also gunite statues of Thai Reishi Yogis practicing the various Asana or traditional Yoga postures - The Thai variation of Hatha Yoga or self treatment. In the past there were more than 100 of these interesting figures scattered about the courtyards of Wat Po. However, over the years many were damaged or deteriorated due to weathering and have been retired for preservation. The Yoga of the Thai Reishi is referred to as *Reusi Dottan*.

In Thailand's past, the people came to the temples for just about everything from medical help to education. Anyone could come to the temple for food, shelter, medical or spiritual healing. ITTM (Traditional Thai Medicine/ Traditional Thai Massage) contributed to the emotional, physical and spiritual well being of the ancient Thais, and it continues to do so today.

Thai culture as a whole is a blending of many cultures from east to west (India to China and from Tibet to Indonesia) and ITTM reflects this. In the present day, there are two primary schools of indigenous traditiona

Thai medicine and indigenous traditional Thai massage (Thai Yoga) and several minor. As well there are many private teachers and monks or nuns passing on multi-generational teachings in the oral tradition. Many of these having grown up in families practicing for several generations, are very knowledgeable.

It is relatively recent in Thailand's history (1990's), that the Royal Thai Government under various ministries has shown interest and made dedicated efforts to catalog the various traditional schools and teachers from the entire country. Initially the emphasis was on the "official" or Bangkok styles and schools and over the years wider research has involved many more variations. There is now standardized practice and curriculum for the traditional practices under the Union of Thai Traditional Medicine Society (UTTS) which has been recognized by the United Nations formally as the Indigenous Traditional Medicine of Thailand (1978: WHO UN DESA, recognition Indigenous and Traditional Medicine).

There are famous and well known traditional schools such as the Traditional College of Medicine, Wat Pho, Bangkok Wat Raja Orasanam, Thonburi; Anantasuk School of

Thai Traditional Medicine: Wiangklaikangwan Industrial College: Hua Hin and Lak Sii (Aachan, Phaa Khruu Anantasuk); Ayurved Vidyalai: Bangkok and the Foundation of Shivago Komarpaj, Buntautuk Old Medical Hospital in Chiang Mai (Founded by Aachan Sintorn Chaichagun in 1973). There are also satellite or derivative medical schools in the Wat Potradition in various areas of the country outside of Bangkok located in Lamphun and Chiang Mai.

Indigenous, Traditional Thai Medicine and Massage is also taught in other local temples, temple auxiliaries and by various competent individuals from Chiang Mai to Sri Lanka. I refer to the Wat Sawankhalok Medicine School for the Blind (Aachan Tawee), The School of Traditional Medicine at Wat Suandok in Chiang Mai, and Wat Amperwa, as well as in traditional sword fighting schools such as the Buddhai Swan Institute formerly located in Nongkham and now in Ayutthaya. The practices of ITTM are found in the Muay Boran and Muay Thai Boxing Traditions. Lastly, you see the practices and Ayurvedic influences in the *Reusi Dottan* or "Reishi/Yogi" still practiced and currently experiencing a renewed interest.

PLEASE NOTE: Today the official designation of the Indigenous, Traditional Thai Medicine abbreviation in common use is TTM. For the purposes of this book, as we wish to emphasize the indigenous and traditional origins of both what is formally recognized and the oral traditional practices passed on and in common use by family, tribal and temple institutions, we will use ITTM.

Much progress has been made towards formal recognition of ITTM in Thailand. It is now officially recognized with parity of its primary competitors the institutional and or corporate based western Allopathic medicine and that of Traditional Chinese Medicine. The Thai government defines the highest standard on ITTM practitioners i.e. Traditional Doctors (*Moh Boran* and or *Moh Phaen Boran*) as those "practicing the healing arts by means of knowledge gained from traditional text or study which is not based on science." [22][23][24][26][27].

This is not to say that the essentially traditional practices are unscientific! Many aspects and uses of ITTM for the reduction of suffering and the curing of disease have been clinically verified in published scientific articles and clinical trials.

Today's path for formal recognition in Traditional Thai Medicine (TTM) [24] Traditional Doctor follows a rigorous and defined course of study and National examinations followed by licensing.[27] Training duration, depending on area of specialization can be anywhere from two to four or more years. This is due to the long catalog of traditional areas of specialization from the Hands-on/Chirothesia to practices of Midwifery, Bone Setting, Herbal Medicine and more. The historical records appear to concur that from the earliest time the practice of medicine and traditional healing was a sacred act, performed by individuals obligated under oath to perform healing as a spiritual practice and sacred duty.

Origins of the Thai people

There is some controversy and differing opinions as to the historical origins of the Thai people who came to found the country of Thailand. Formerly the country was called Siam, a designation which likely originated with the Portuguese, who were among the first westerners to visit the region.

Some historians estimate that the origin of the Thai people is in the north of what we today call Siberia. In a latter period, these people immigrated in a southerly direction and eventually settled in China in an area from the Huang Ho River downward. About 2,500 years before the Buddhist Era (about 4,500 years ago) displaced Chinese people crossed the Thien Cham Mountain and began to infiltrate the basin of the Huang Ho River. They met the "Ai Lao" or "Thai" people there. The Chinese called these people "Tai" meaning powerful and prosperous. The Thai themselves have always preferred to refer to themselves as "Meung Thai."

Recently, however, this migratory theory has been challenged by the discovery of prehistoric artifacts in the village of Ban Chiang in the Nong Han District of Udon Thani province in the Northeast [28]. There is evidence of bronze metallurgy going back 3,500 years, as well as other indications of a far more sophisticated culture than any previously suspected by archaeologists.

Based on these discoveries a new origin theory has been proposed; the Thais may have originated here in Thailand and later scattered to various parts of Asia, including China!

It is significant to note when talking about the history of Thailand that the Thais were not the first inhabitants of Thailand. Although over time the Thais became dominant through military conquest the majority of their subjects were not Thai. They were the remnants of the Mon/Khmer dynasties that ruled from India to Vietnam. The Mon/Khmer cultures had originally been part of a great Hindu empire that stretched from Tibet to the Philippines by way of South and Southeast Asia. Historically this Hindu empire dating back to the lifetime of the Buddha (500 BCE) was known as the Majapahit (Maharlika) empire (Virgil Apostal: Way of the Ancient Healers). Thai rulers in their expansion and southward migration gradually adopted many of the ways and cultures of the people they came to rule.

According to researchers (Braun and Schumacher: Traditional Herbal Medicine in Northern Thailand: White Lotus 1994) [2] "The Thai Court followed a pattern of adopting (and adapting) the indianized culture of the people they conquered. During the Ayutthaya period Indian influence thus became firmly established in many domains: the concept of divine kingship replaced the original Thai version of feudalism; Indian Law - The Code of Manu - became the model for Thai law; The astrologers surrounding the king were Hindus; the alphabet was modeled after Indian (and Khmer alphabets); Indian literary genres and metrics were introduced and of course Buddhism became the national religion.

Please note: The Thai did not entirely abandon their original Chinese influenced heritage, according to Braun and Schumacher and other sources (Andaya, Reid, Wyatt, Wood). The Thai Kings up to relatively recently, this last century, looked to the emperors of China for official recognition. They maintained relationships formally through tributes made to the Chinese court and through trade. Large numbers of Chinese have always been part of the great migrations into Thailand bringing with them their cultural identities. We can see the Chinese influence in *Wat Raja-Orasarem (Korat)* and in Wat Po (Ayudthaya/ Bangkok) temple design. *Wat Raja-Orasarem* is literally a Chinese style temple built according to Feng Shui principles with eight sides, large circular doors, Chinese style mosaic decoration throughout and a grand multi-tiered pagoda right in the middle. Wat Po has adjacent to the Reclining Buddha statue an actual Taoist shrine and large guardian statues in the Chinese style posted at all entrances and exits.

The Thais apparently split up into two main groups as they traveled along the southern part of China. One group eventually settled in the area of what is now Northern Thailand establishing the Lanna kingdom. The second group settled further south and after being conquered by the Khmer (Angkor: Kampuchea) founded the kingdom of Sukhothai.

The Thai united and set up a large territory which they called "Narn Chao." They controlled this area from approximately 648/B.E. 1192 to 1253/B.E. 1797, for a total of about 600 years. The Chinese continued to press the Thai people until finally a famous Chinese emperor, Ng Quan Lee Cho or Kublai Khan, lead a large army against the Narn Chao and conquered the territory. Most of the Thai's fled further South, although there are still ethnic Thai people in the area of Yunnan China today.

The remaining Thai people settled in the area which they now predominate and set up independent kingdoms (Ngoenyang, Sukhothai, Chiang Mai, Lanna) much like those of India of the same period. These kingdoms were assimilated into the kingdom of Ayudhya around 1369/B.E. 1913.

Krungthep Dvaravati Sri Ayutthaya (also spelled Ayudhya, Ayudthaya or Ayuthia) was capital of Thailand for 417 years under 33 kings of the Ayudhya Dynasty. At its peak, this capital was larger and cleaner than contemporary European capitals. Ayudhya was founded on an island bordered by the Lopburi River on the North, the Pasak River on the East, and the Chao Phyra River to the West and South.

In the 11th century A.D., before the Thai settled, there existed a small outpost settlement formed and named Ayudhya by the Khmer who dominated this region of the Menam Chao Phraya. Ayudhya was of some importance because it formed a boundary with the U-Thong (a vassal State under the Sukhothai - the first integrated Thai kingdom called the "Cradle of Thai Civilization"). The first King of Ayudhya was Somdej Phra Ramathibodi. The kingdom was ruled in succession by 33 kings for 417 years, from A.D. 1350 to A.D. 1767.

Royal Chedi at Ayudthaya (World Heritage Site)

When the original buildings of the new capital were completed in A.D. 1353, King Ramathibodi built the temple Wat Buddhai Swan on the site of his first residence at Wienglak. It is this wat or temple which became the home and training ground for the Kabri-Kabrong Fighting Arts. These Arts were practiced by the monks as a form of meditation andphysical exercise, and the monks themselves were responsible for training the royal family and the military. Essentially, this tradition continues to the present day. Similarly, Wat Chetuphon (Wat Po- later rebuilt in Bangkok) was also established as a teaching center for traditional healing and medicinal arts. In addition to the Chinese influence which the Thais brought with them and the integration of the Indian culture via the Mon/Khmer cultures they conquered, there was significant and continuous

migration, trade and exchange directly between all of the neighboring states and cultures such as India, Burma, Malaysia, Indonesia, Cambodia, Laos and as far away as Persia and Japan.

It is said there was one king of the Ayutthaya period whose entire personal retinue of bodyguards were Japanese Samurai! [7] This is part of the Buddhai Sawan history of the development of the Thai Martial Art Kabri-Kabrong which includes the use and techniques appropriate for the Katana and the Thai equivalent the Maha Deo or Great Sword. Phaa Khruu Samaii Mesamarn once gave a lecture on the Japanese influence in Thai Sword fighting and in Thai healing arts saying the Budo arts and Japanese (Chinese) Amma was influential beginning during the Ayutthaya kingdom period. Some of the Samurai allegedly returned to Japan where we suspect they shared Thai teachings of medicine and martial arts as well.

I have two possible examples: 1) The "Extraordinary meridians" of Shiatsu Anma (Massanauga/ Ohashi Schools), which are virtually identical to the depictions and stated functions of Thai Sen Lines. This was corroborated by me in discussions with Dr. Do An Kaneko, PhD researcher, University of Tokyo in 1989 and 1991.

2) Historical accounts of Japanese merchants and Samuri in Ayudthaya from the Twelth century through the fall of the old capital[8] [9] [10] [11]. "*Thai-Japanese Relations in Historical Prospective* (1988), edited by Chavit Khamchoo and E. Bruce Reynolds; and *From Japan to Arabia: Ayudhya's Maritime Relations with Asia* (1999), edited by Kennon Breazeale. From Japan, besides historical material, come numerous tales narrating the adventures of Yamada Nagamasa (ca. 1585-1630), the most prominent Japanese figure in the history of Ayudhya" [7]. Yamada, a Samuri was first famous as a warrior and later in life as a merchant. There was a vibrant Japanses enclave in Ayudthaya for hundreds of years. There were also many accounts of commerce and communications, trade and exchange between the Thai Kings and Japanese Shoguns." It is estimated that the Japanese district, in its heyday of the 1620, counted 1,000 to 1,500 inhabitants[29], making Ayudhya's Nihonmachi the second in population size of the Japanese enclaves in southeast Asia.

To the present day you will see ancient and famous Japanese weapons: Katana, Daisho, Yori etc. in the Royal Museum weapons Armory in Bangkok. Thai Kings in Royal Regalia wear and/or hold a Japanese sword decorated in the ornate Thai style.

Burma was certainly one of the primary sources of cultural influence, however, with a periodically contentious and or warlike relationship. The period of settlement in the old Capital of Ayudhya is significant in that it was marked with numerous altercations and battles with the neighboring country of Burma. The Burmese captured the Capital of Siam (as it was called in 1568/B.E. 2112) and took most of the population as prisoners back to Burma (Myanmar). During this time period, Siam was a vassal State of the Burmese.

Around 1582/B.E. 2126, the Thais, led by the self-declared Thai King Naresuan, revolted against the Burmese. King Naresuan had become famous for being a great boxer or fighter and founder of Buddhai Sawan. King Naresuan and the Burmese Crown Prince met in single combat mounted on elephants. They dueled fiercely and King Naresuan defeated the Prince and the Burmese army was routed. (A monument to both King Narasuan and the Kabri- Kabrong arts is located in Phitsanolaok not far from the night market.) In 1781/B.E. 2325, King Phra Buddha Yodfa Chulaloke ascended the throne as the first King of the Chakri Dynasty. Thailand continued as an independent State from this time to the present day where it is currently under the patronage of H.M. King Bhumibol Adulyadej, ninth King of the Chakri Dynasty. The capital of Thailand presently is Krungthep or Bangkok, where the King resides in the Grand Palace next to Wat Phra Kaeo, the Temple of the Emerald Buddha, and Wat Pho, the Temple of the Reclining Buddha.

Khmer/Mon/Sumatra/Majapahit Cultural Influence

The influence of the Indianized Khmer/Mon culture in all aspects of traditional life in much of the central and western regions of Thailand should not be underestimated. Most aspects of life reflected this influence including the colloquial traditional medicine practices of the era. For a little over 300 years Mon/Khmer and Sumatra culture was the dominant culture of the region. Khmer culture was a Vedic culture, revering the Hindu art, culture, and text of classical India including the practice of traditional or classical Ayurveda.

Khmer style architecture and decorative detail: Srisatchanali/ Sukhotai

According to the World Health Organization (WHO) Legal Status of Traditional Medicine and Complementary/Alternative Medicine: The use of traditional medicine is documented in the stone inscription of the King Chaivoraman (around 1182-1186) who ruled the Khmer Kingdom (Thai/Cambodia) which is in the northeastern part of Thailand. Traditional medicine was used in one hundred and two hospitals which, at that time, was called 'Arogaya sala'.[25] [31] "

It can be inferred that Khmer doctors practiced Ayurveda and Vedic medical astrology (Jyotish). Remnants of this practice may be seen today in the Anantasuk TTM practice of medical astrology (Anantasuk Korosot) as taught at the Wiangklaikangwan Industrial College TTM curriculum in Hua Hin.

From the 9th to the 11th century, the central and western area of Thailand was occupied by the Mon civilization called Dvaravati. The Mon share the same common lineage as the Khmer and settle in southern Burma later. The influence of Dvaravati includes Nakhon Pathom, Khu Bua, Phong Tuk, and Lawo (Lopburi). Dvaravati was Indianized culture, Theravada Buddhism remained the major religion in this area.

After 1157 CE [25](Chockevivat, Chuthaputti, Chamchoy), Mon heavily influenced central Thailand. Khmer cultural influence was brought in the form of language, art and religion. The "Sanskrit" language entered in Mon-Thai vocabulary during the Khmer or Lopburi Period. The influence of this period has affected many provinces in the north-east such as Kanchanaburi and Lopburi.

The Architecture in "Angkor" was also constructed according to the Khmer style. The Khmer built stone temples in the northeast, some of which have been restored to their former glory, those at Phimai and Phanom Rung and further cultures are stone sculptures and stone Buddha images. Politically, however, the Khmer cultural dominance did not control the whole area but exercised power and cultural influence through vassals and governors." [32]

Sumatra/Sumatran culture, a Buddhist culture until the 1300's when it became officially Muslim, controlled or ruled southern Thailand and especially peninsular and coastal Thailand. Originally called the Melayu Kingdom (Malayu, Dharmasraya Kingdom or Jambi), it was absorbed by the Kingdom of Srivijaya. Sumatra was a vassal state in the Majapahit Empire which stretched from Sumatra to New Guinea. The Indianized Sumatran/Majapahit culture and trade were certainly factors in early Thai history from the Ayutthaya and Bangkok periods first simply because these were the culture and belief systems of the indigenous people who lived there before being assimilated into the Thai Kingdom and secondly due to trade and exchange. The common traditional medicine of the Majapahit was Ayurveda and their famous martial arts were based on Kalaripayattu. Thai Kings, traders and military would have encountered all of them! The vast Majapahit Empire controlled the seas and trade routes of the Asian, SE Asian, Malaysian, and Indonesian archipelago all the way to the Philippines. Keep in mind trade is a two way system and ancient trade always included medicine and medicine practices.

The history and research I have given here is far from complete! My intention is to give the reader/ student a background and context for the birth and development of the Royal Thai Traditional Medicine and Healing system (Indigenous, Traditional Thai Medicine: Indigenous, Traditional Thai Massage: ITTM) which we simply call the Southern or Royal style and the practices of "Reusi Dottan", Thai Reishi Yoga which are part of it.

Part One

Benefits

Practice Overview

Practice Guide

Benefits

SUMMARY AND DESCRIPTION

The techniques described in this manual, if performed properly and on a regular basis, can help to maintain inner well being, balance energy, relax the whole body and strengthen the soft and or connective tissues restoring and or maintaining the health of the the Arms and Upper Torso: most specifically focused on the fingers, wrists and shoulder girdle. These techniques are also all together a form of Chi Gung/ Prana Healing.

A few of the benefits of the practice may include:

Increased blood flow to the fingers, hands, wrists, arms and shoulders

Reduced fatigue/increased energy levels

Improved respiration quality (when performed with proper breathing)

Improved lymphatic function

Reduced toxicity and residual metabolic wastes

Increased available anti-oxidants

Reduced accumulation of free radicals

Reduced edema and swelling

Reduced pain and sensitivity

Reduced calcification and bone spurring caused by poor or reduced circulation and or atrophy and or strain injuries

Reduced possibility of secondary infections from chronic diseases such as diabetes

Reduced fungal infections of the hands and nails

Practice Overview

The practice consists of 23 hand, Shoulder and wrist stretching techniques that are performed in a pre-defined sequence.

There are two options for practicing: the SHORT session and the FULL session. -
(See pages following for descriptions.)

GUIDING PRINCIPLES

     Stand with your feet shoulder width apart, knees slightly bent.

     Inhale during the preparation phase and exhale slowly when stretching.

     Move slowly and deliberately-no sudden movements.

     Do not over-stretch-stop and/or release the posture if you feel intense pain.

     Hold each position for a minimum of five to ten seconds, then return to neutral.

     After completing each round (warm up through closing sequence), check in and notice how your arms,
          wrists and shoulders feel for approximately 30 seconds; then proceed to the next round.

TIP: Set a regular schedule for practice; a short session each day will be more beneficial than a long session
       at infrequent intervals.

LIST OF HAND THERAPY TECHNIQUES

WARM UP	MAIN SEQUENCE	OPTIONAL TECHNIQUES	CLOSING SEQUENCE
Swing Arms	Inward Wrist Lock	Bird's Beak	Shake wrists
Arm Circles	Elbow Squeeze	Tiger's Claw	Clap
Wrist Circles	Outward Wrist Lock	Make Fist (Three Positions)	Drop and Breathe
Shake Hands	Palm Up/Fold Down	Knife Hand Circles	Check-In
	Over and Under	Rocking Fists	
	Elbow Lever Pull	Phoenix Eye	
	Straight Arm Lock		
	Overhead Shoulder Stretch		
	Stop Position/ Five-Finger Pull		
	Squeeze and Extend		
	Tight Fist Circles		
	Open Wrist Circles		
	Tan Sao Series		

Practice Guide

SHORT SESSION

In the short session practice, the practitioner performs three rounds of practice. (*See Figure 1 right and Example 1 below*)

In the first round, the practitioner performs the warm up, then the main sequence **Positions 1** through **5** and **Position 13** (a flowing sequence of seven different techniques), and the closing sequence.

In the second and third rounds the practitioner completes the warm up and **Positions 1** through **5**. The practitioner then chooses one of the *optional techniques* before completing the closing sequence.

TIP: *All the techniques described in this book may be done kneeling and or sitting as well.*

Figure 1: SHORT SESSION

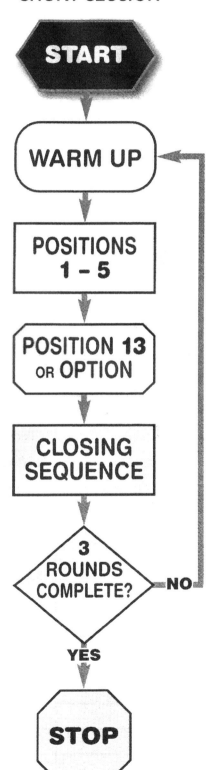

Figure 1:
SHORT SESSION

ROUND ONE	ROUND TWO	ROUND THREE
SWING ARMS	SWING ARMS	SWING ARMS
ARM CIRCLES	ARM CIRCLES	ARM CIRCLES
WRIST CIRCLES	WRIST CIRCLES	WRIST CIRCLES
SHAKE HANDS	SHAKE HANDS	SHAKE HANDS
MAIN SE-QUENCE	MAIN SE-QUENCE	MAIN SE-QUENCE
INWARD WRIST LOCK	INWARD WRIST LOCK	INWARD WRIST LOCK
ELBOW SQUEEZE	ELBOW SQUEEZE	ELBOW SQUEEZE
OUTWARD WRIST LOCK	OUTWARD WRIST LOCK	OUTWARD WRIST LOCK
PALM UP/ FOLD DOWN	PALM UP/ FOLD DOWN	PALM UP/ FOLD DOWN
OVER AND UN-DER	OVER AND UN-DER	OVER AND UN-DER
TAN SAO SERIES	*BIRDS BEAK*	*TIGER'S CLAW*
CLOSING SEQUENCE	CLOSING SEQUENCE	CLOSING SEQUENCE
SHAKE WRIST	SHAKE WRIST	SHAKE WRIST
CLAP	CLAP	CLAP
DROP & BREATHE	DROP & BREATHE	DROP & BREATHE
CHECK IN	CHECK IN	CHECK IN

Practice Guide
FULL SESSION

In the full session practice, the practitioner performs six rounds and uses all of the techniques. (*See Figure 2 right and Example 2 below*)

In the first round, the practitioner performs the warm up, then the mainsequence **Positions 1** through **13**, and the closing sequence.

In rounds two through six, the practitioner performs the warm up, then the main sequence **Positions 1** through **12**. The practitioner then substitutes one of the optional techniques in turn at position **13** for repetitions two through six.

Example 2: FULL SESSION

ROUND ONE	ROUND TWO
WARM UP	WARM UP
Swing Arms	Main Sequence 1 - 12
Arm Circles	*Birds Beak*
Wrist Circles	CLOSING SEQUENCE
Shake Hands	**ROUND THREE**
MAIN SEQUENCE	WARM UP
1 Inward Wrist Lock	**MAIN SEQUENCE 1 - 12**
2 Elbow Squeeze	*Tiger's Claw*
3 Outward Wrist Lock	CLOSING SEQUENCE
4 Palm Up/ Fold Down	**ROUND FOUR**
5 Over and Under	WARM UP
6 Elbow Lever Pull	**MAIN SEQUENCE 1 - 12**
7 Straight Arm Lock	*Make Fist (Three Positions)*
8 Overhead Shoulder Stretch	CLOSING SEQUENCE
9 Five-Finger Pull	**ROUND FIVE**
10 Squeeze and Extend	WARM UP
11 Tight Fist Circles	**MAIN SEQUENCE 1 - 12**
12 Open Wrist Circles	*Knife Hand Circles*
13 *Tan Sao Series*	CLOSING SEQUENCE
CLOSING SEQUENCE	**ROUND SIX**
Shake wrists	WARM UP
Clap	**MAIN SEQUENCE 1 - 12**
Drop and Breathe	*Rocking Fist or Phoenix Eye*
Check-In	CLOSING SEQUENCE

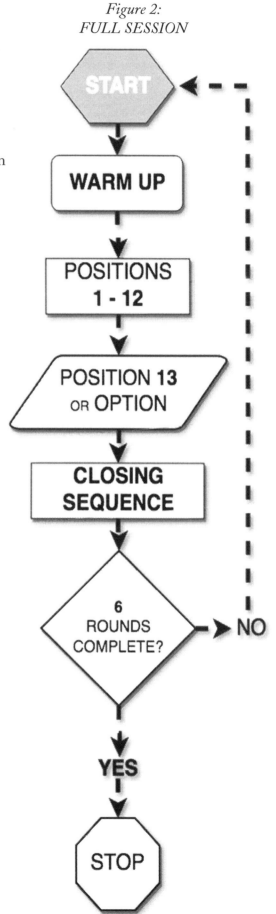

Figure 2:
FULL SESSION

NOTES:

Part Two

THE PRACTICE

Figure 1:
SHORT SESSION

Figure 2:
FULL SESSION

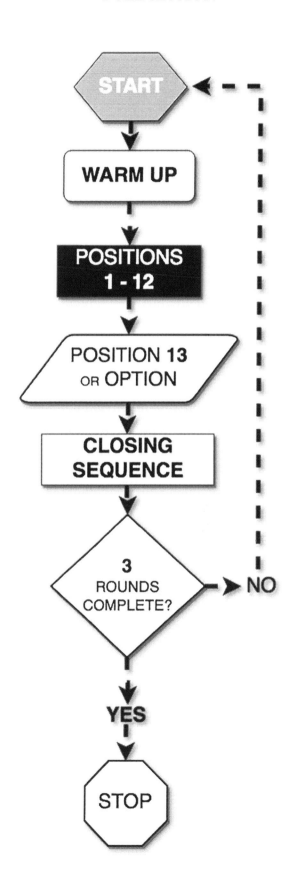

Warm Up Sequence

SWING ARMS

 1 Stand with your hands shoulder width apart, knees slightly bent.

2 Swing your arms slowly, twisting your body and looking in the direction of turn. Hands should contact your upper hip on the opposite side.

3 Swing 10 limes each way.

ARM CIRCLES

 Stand with your hands shoulder width apart and knees slightly bent.

 Raise your arms to the front and then overhead, making a circle behind you while keeping your hands wide apart in front and as close as possible in the back.

Repeat 10 times

Extend your arms behind you and then overhead, making a circle while keeping your arms straight and your hands as close as possible behind you and wide apart in front.

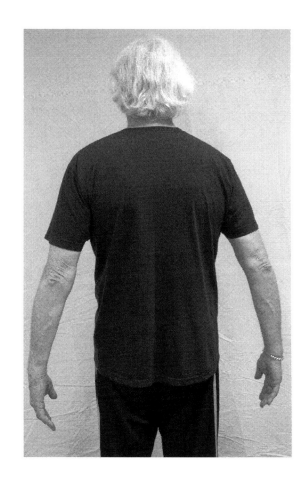

Repeat 10 times.

WRIST CIRCLES

Rotate your wrists extending
to your full range of motion
10 times each way.

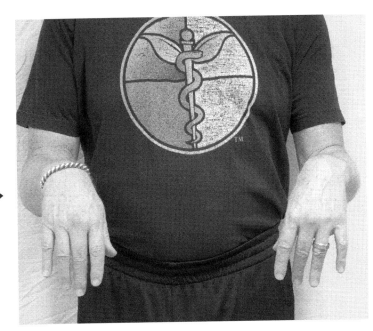

Shake hands lightly.

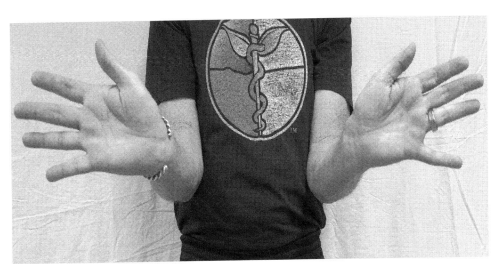

NOTES

Figure 1:
SHORT SESSION

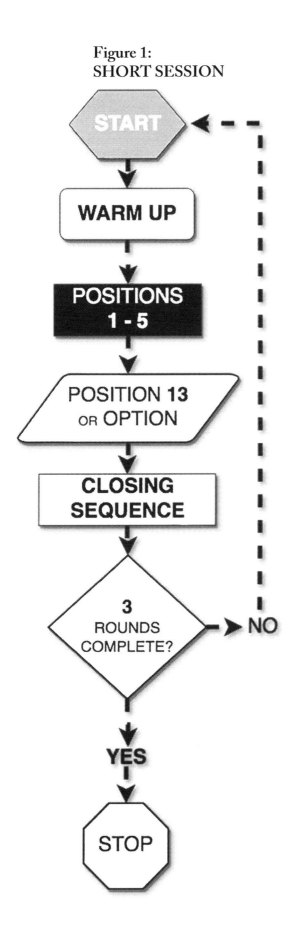

Figure 2:
FULL SESSION

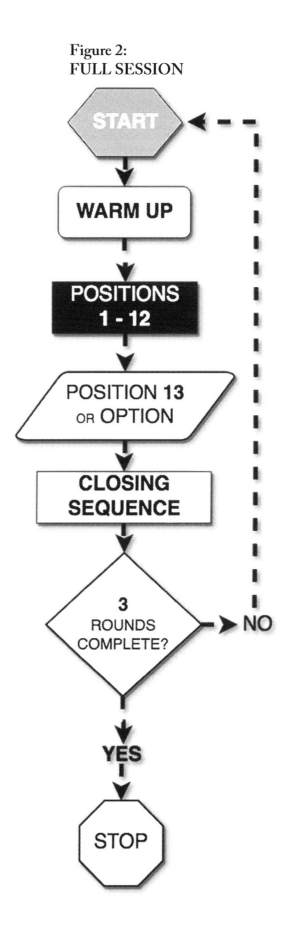

MAIN SEQUENCE

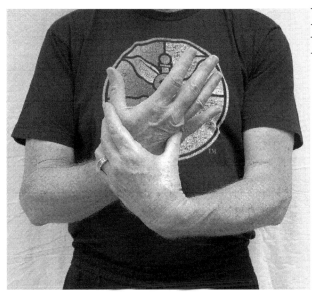

Position 1
INWARD WRIST LOCK

 Cross your hands in front of your chest even with the breast plate (sternum), palms facing inward and elbows tight to your body, right hand closest to the body.

Grasp the back of the right hand with the palm of the left hand and wrap the fingers of the left hand around the base of the right thumb. Place the thumb of the left hand at the base of the ring finger on the back of the right hand.

Twist the pinky finger of the right hand toward the center line of the body.

Hand position detail.

Inhale and drop both hands as far as possible, elbows out with arms close to the body. Apply light pressure to the right wrist by twisting right hand to the right, pulling with the fingers while pushing with the thumb;
Hold for five to 10 seconds.

 Inhale, release, return to the starting position, switch hands and repeat on the opposite side. Inhale, release and shake hands lightly.

Position 2
ELBOW SQUEEZE

Bring the forearms up parallel with the collar bone, fingers pointing toward the opposite elbow. Place the right palm on the back of the left hand

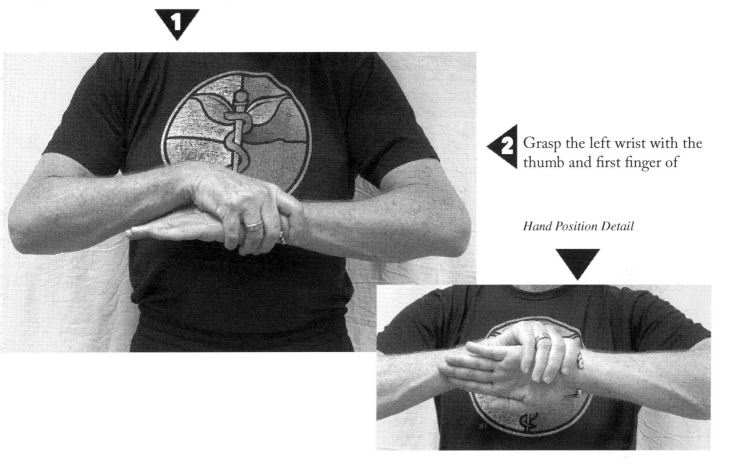

Grasp the left wrist with the thumb and first finger of

Hand Position Detail

Inhale, then exhale and drop the elbows toward each other. Squeeze the elbows together while holding the left wrist firmly with the right hand. Hold for five to 10 seconds.

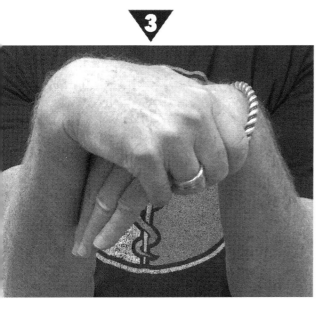

Inhale and raise the elbows to the starting position, reverse hand position and repeat. Inhale, release and shake hands lightly.

Position 3
OUTWARD WRIST LOCK

Raise the right arm, forearm parallel to the collar bone, turn the wrist to point the fingers away from the body.

Grasp the top of the right hand with the left hand, fingers and thumb on top of the knife edge of the right hand.

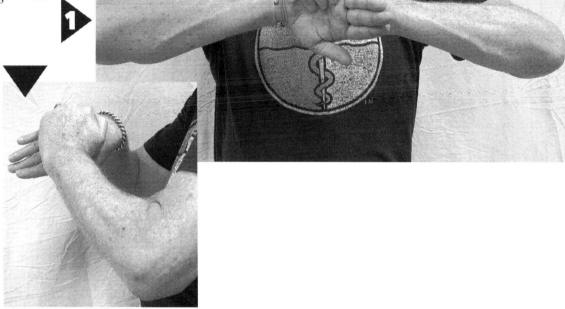

Hand position detail.

Exhale, dropping the right elbow down and inward toward the floor until it locks. Pull the top of the right hand with the left hand until the wrist locks.

Hold for five to 10 seconds.

Inhale while releasing and switch position. Inhale, release and shake hands lightly.

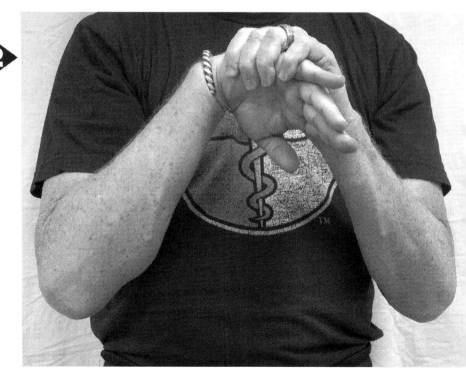

Position 4
PALM UP - FOLD DOWN

Bring the right elbow to the center line of the body, palm facing away from the body, fingers together pointing down. Place the left hand across the right hand at a right angle.

Tan Sao Position

Inhale, then exhale and pull the fingers of the right hand down and back toward the body.
Inhale, release and repeat. Shake hands lightly on release.

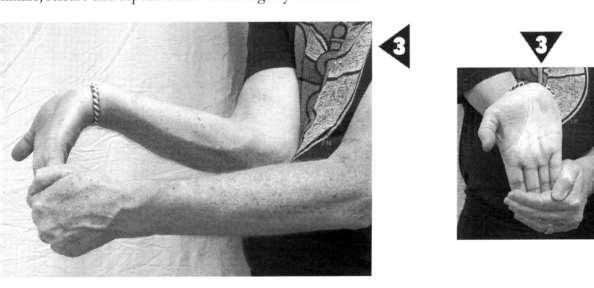

Variation: Pull each finger individually back and downward toward the body.

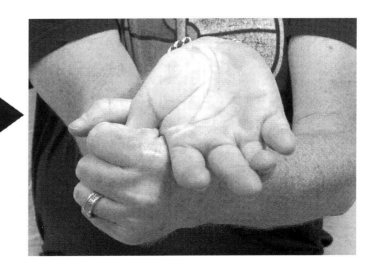

Position 5
OVER AND UNDER

Place the right elbow along the center line of the body, right palm up, arm outstretched at a 45-degree angle from the body.

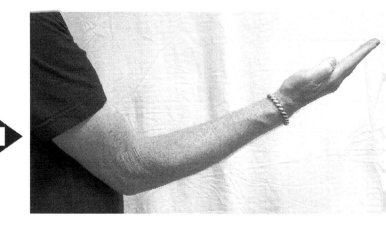

1

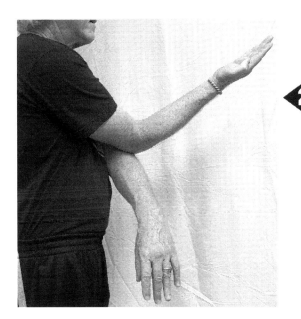

2 Bring the left elbow adjacent to the right elbow.

Table top

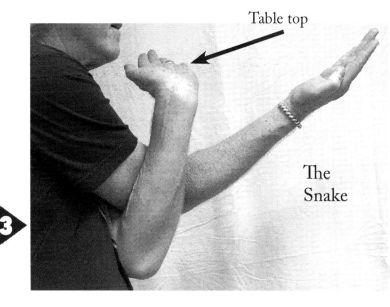

The Snake

Reach across the body, under the right elbow with the left arm and rotate the left arm up, creating the "table" with the left hand.

3

4

4

Fold the right hand back onto the "Table" hand. Grasp firmly grasp the top of the right hand with the left hand (Table hand). Once in position Pull up on the right arm with the left forearm while pushing down with the right hand to rotate the right shoulder toward the floor. Stabilize the elbow and try not to lean!

Hold for five to 10 seconds. Bend at the waist for a deeper stretch.

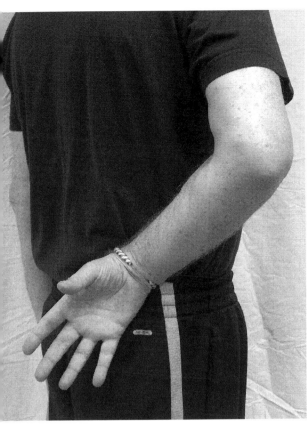

Position 6
ELBOW LEVER AND PULL

Place the back of the right wrist on the back of right hip. Reach across the body with the left hand and grasp the right elbow.

Inhale, then exhale and pull with the left arm, rotating the right arm toward the front center-line of the body.

Hold for five to 10 seconds.

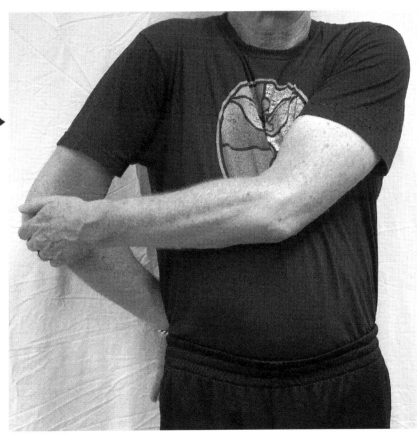

Inhale, release, switch positions and repeat. Release and shake hands lightly.

Position 7
STRAIGHT ARM LOCK

Interlock the fingers behind the back, arms pointing toward the floor-wrists and elbows as close together as possible.

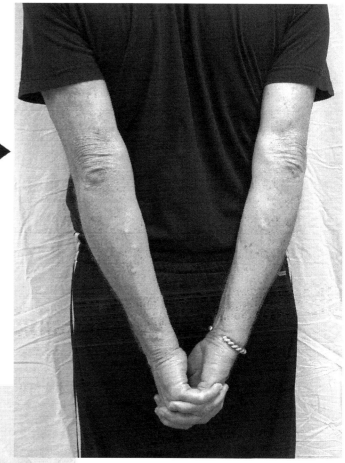

Push down with wrists locked and straight, inhale, then exhale extending forward and bending at the waist, bringing the arms up and over toward the floor.

Hold for five to 10 seconds.

Inhale and return to upright position Release and shake hands lightly.

Position 8
OVERHEAD SHOULDER STRETCH

 Place the right palm on the center of the back, elbow vertical, fingers pointing toward the floor. Reach overhead with the left arm and grasp the right elbow.

Inhale, then exhale and push the right elbow to extend the right hand toward the floor. Creep down the spine with fingertips.

Hold for five to 10 seconds.

 Advanced Variation: Tuck the elbow of the opposite arm behind the back, with the back of the hand against the body and fingers pointing toward the head. Reach up, curl the fingers of both hands, hooking the arms together, and pull the upper arm down gently.

Inhale and release, switch positions and repeat. Shake hands lightly.

Position 9
FIVE-FINGER PULL

Extend one arm in front of the body,
palm facing away as if stopping traffic.

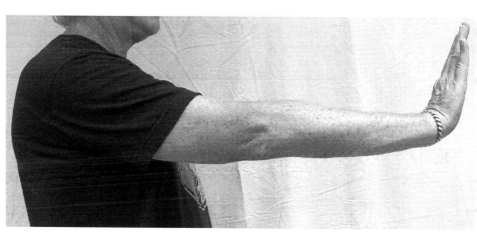

 Reach across with the opposite hand and grasp the little finger of
the extended hand. Pull each finger individually back towards the
body. Hold for five to 10 seconds, exhaling with each pull.

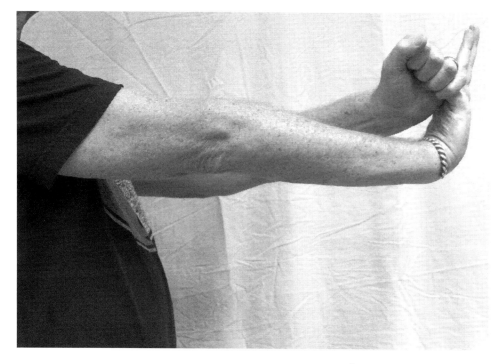

Reverse positions and repeat. Shake hands lightly.

Position 10
SQUEEZE AND EXTEND

1 Keeping both elbows close to the body, raise both hands to waist height, palms facing each other.

2 Make fists with both hands and squeeze for a count of three think *tighter, tighter, tighter.*

3 Pop fingers out quickly try to spread and extend or make longer for three counts-think *wider, wider, wider.*

4 Repeat ten times. Release and shake hands lightly.

Position 11
TIGHT FIST CIRCLES

Keeping both elbows close to the body, raise both hands to waist height, palms facing each other.

Make fists with both hands.

Keeping tight fists, rotate (make circles) 10 times each way-extending   through the full range of motion. Do not move the arms.

Release and shake hands lightly.

Position 12
OPEN WRIST CIRCLES

Repeat **Position 11** with open hands, fingers loose. Moving slowly, flex and extend the wrists through the full range of motion.

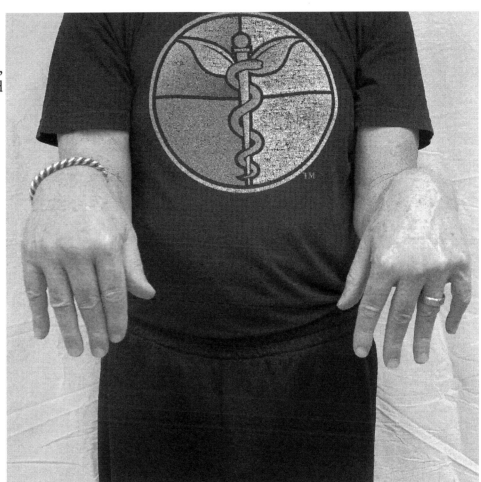

Position 13•1
TAN SAO

Elbows tucked into the waist; hands
extended at a 45-degree angle away
from the body, palms facing up.

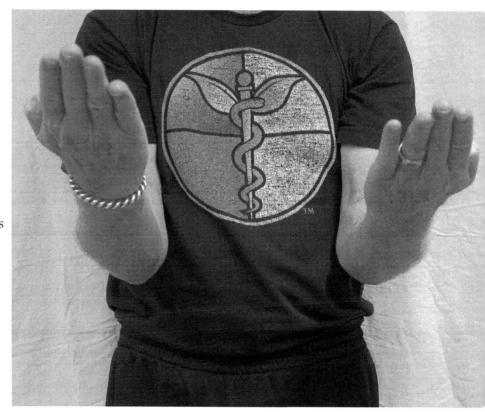

Position 13•2
BON SAO

Rotate elbows outward, palms facing
outward, wrists flexed. Exhale,
lower the elbows toward the floor
while keeping the wrists close
together.

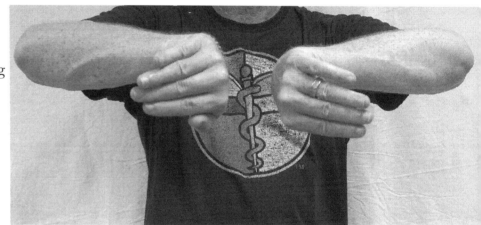

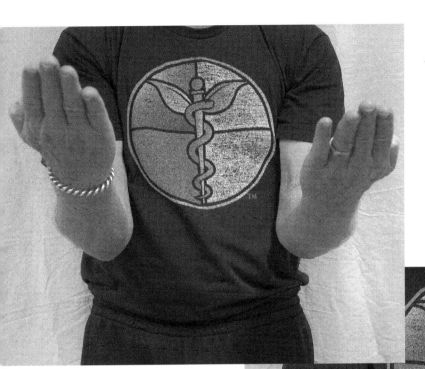

Position 13•3
TAN SAO

Positions 13•4 and 13•5
DITJAO

(Begin) Rotate the palms to face each other, make tight fists with both hands.

13 • 4

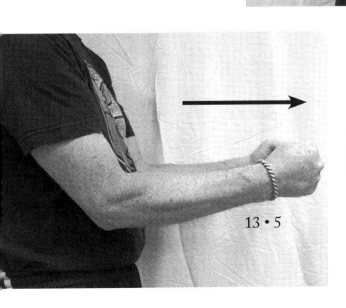

13 • 5

(End) Elbows tucked into the waist, exhale and extend tight fists away from the body slowly.

Return to first position. Repeat Position 13•1.

Positions
13•6 and 13•7
FUKSAO

(Begin) Open fists and turn palms toward the floor.

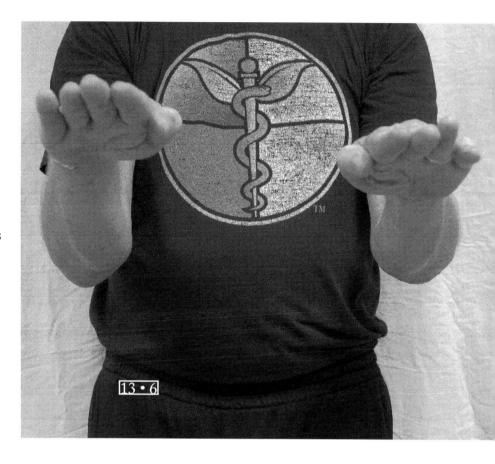

(End) Try to touch the forearm with the fingers while pulling the elbows back to the waist.

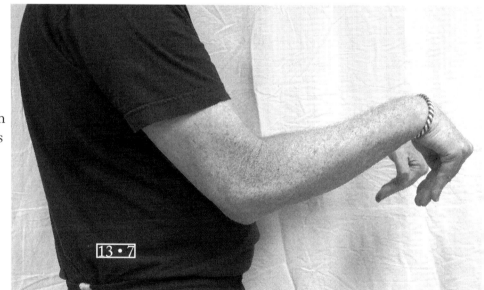

NOTES

Figure 1: SHORT SESSION

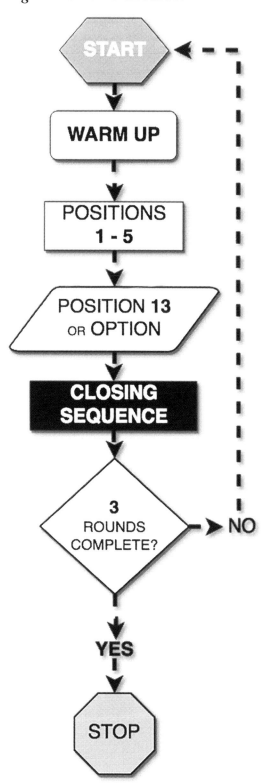

Figure 2: FULL SESSION

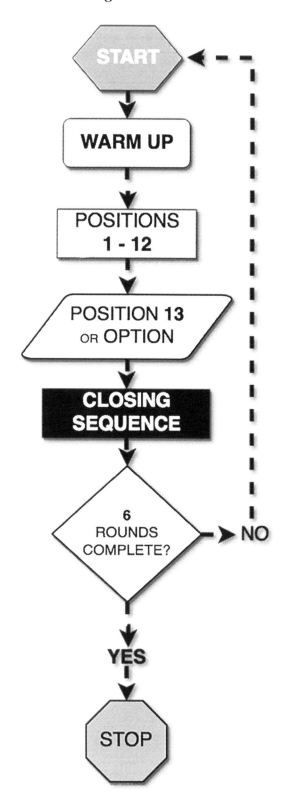

CLOSING SEQUENCE

Position 14
SHAKE WRISTS

Shake wrists vigorously while bringing the hands close to the ears, "hear the wind".

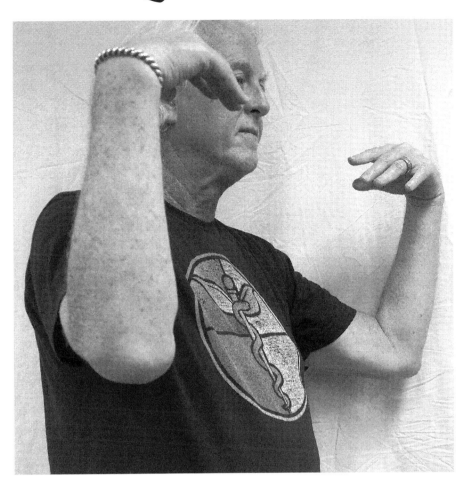

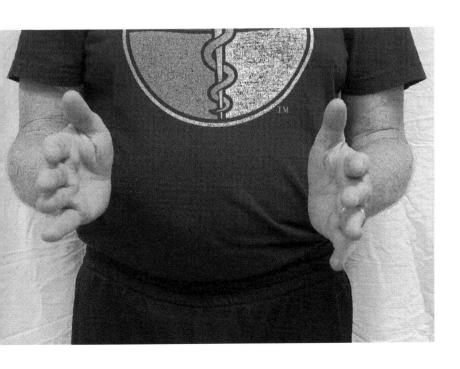

Position 15
CLAP HANDS

Bring attention and energy to your clapping your hands together sharply.

Position 16
DROP AND BREATHE

Drop and breathe normally one breath
 as the hands come down (let arms collapse).

Breathe normally for several breaths.

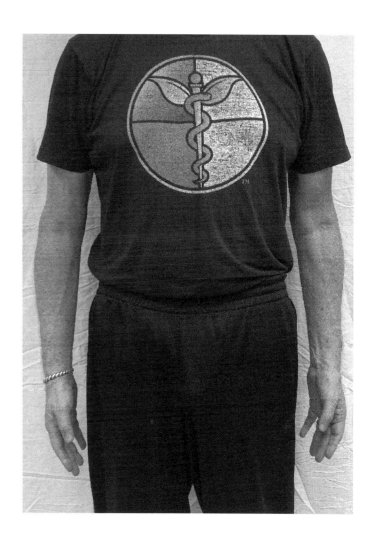

Position 17
CHECK-IN

Check-in- feel your pulse and bring awareness to your hands, shoulders, etc.

Figure 1: SHORT SESSION

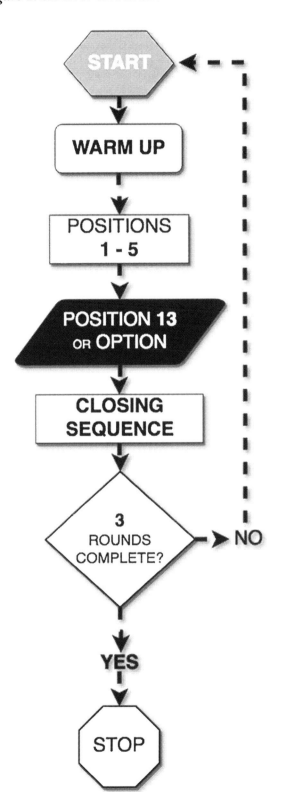

Figure 2: FULL SESSION

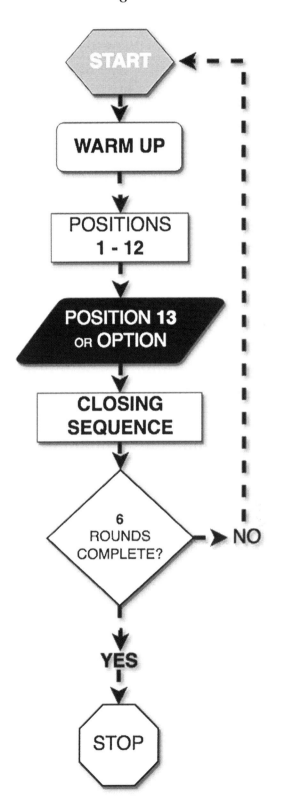

CLOSING SEQUENCE

Position 18
BIRD'S BEAK

Elbows in tight against the body, arms pointing straight upwards with palms forward.

1

Extend fingers forward, purse together and squeeze tightly 10 times.

2

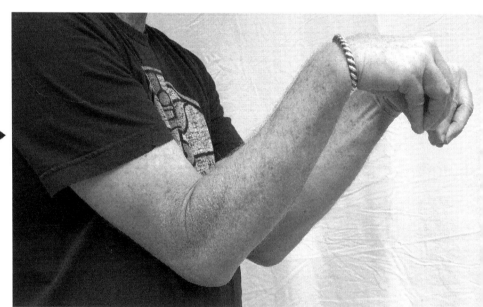

Position 19
TIGER'S CLAW

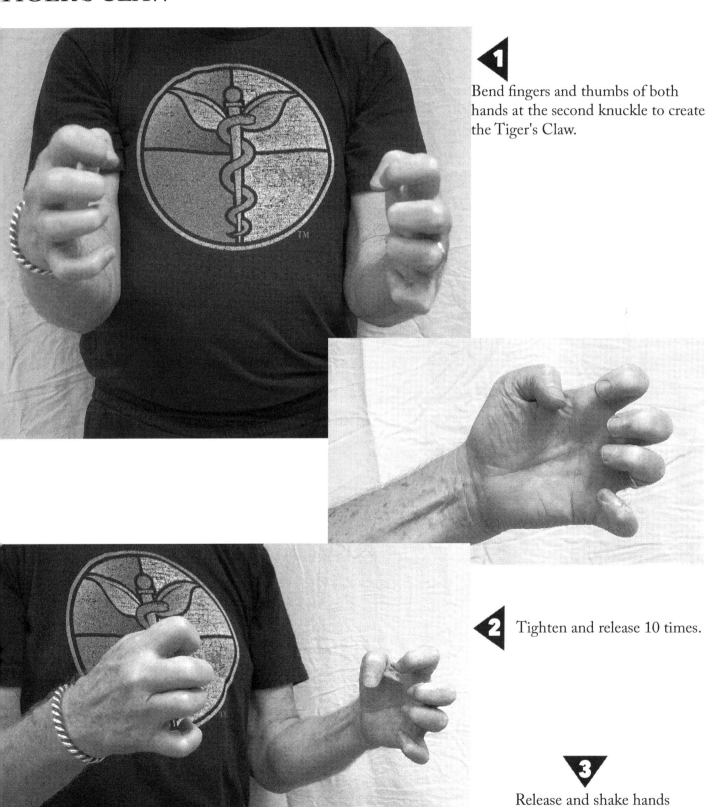

1 Bend fingers and thumbs of both hands at the second knuckle to create the Tiger's Claw.

2 Tighten and release 10 times.

3 Release and shake hands lightly.

Position 20
MAKE FISTS

Make fists with both hands in three steps:

Fold fingers at the
second knuckle.

 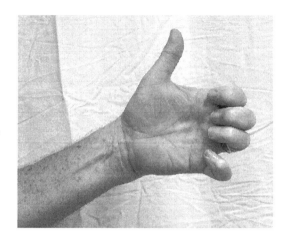

Fold fingers to the
center of the hand.

 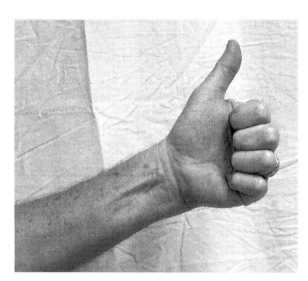

Wrap thumbs

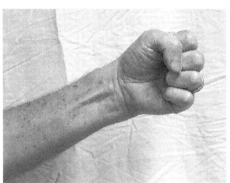

Open and close using three steps

10 times, squeezing tightly each time.

Position 21
KNIFE HAND CIRCLES

Hold hands in front of the body with the palms facing each other in a knife hand.

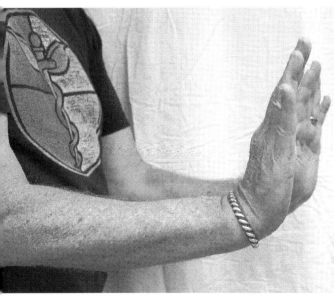

Keeping the knife hand tight-rotate the hands 10 times each way.

Release and shake hands lightly.

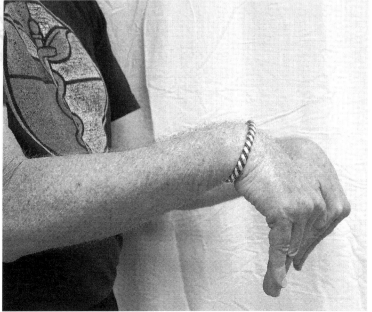

Position 22
ROCKING FISTS

Make fists with both hands, forearms parallel to the floor at waist height.

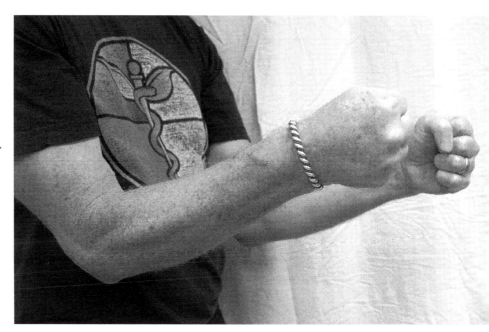

Rock the fist forward and backward 10 times, alternately pointing both thumbs toward the floor and ceiling.

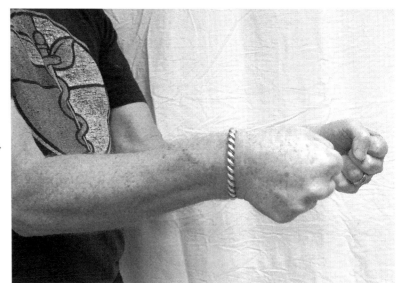

Release and shake hands lightly.

Position 23
PHOENIX EYE

Make fists with both hands

Squeeze and extend each finger individually in turn using the adjacent finger to create resistance.

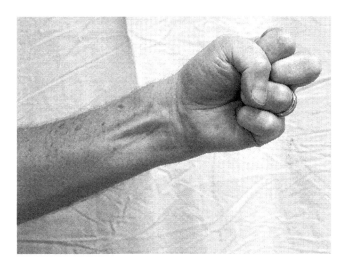

Reverse directions and repeat.

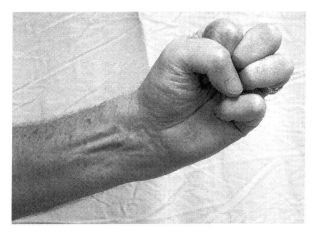

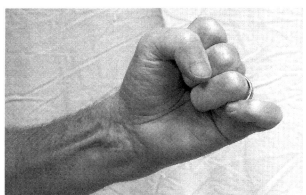

NOTES

BIBLIOGRAPHY

[1] Nuat Thai, Traditional Thai Medical Massage…

[2] Brun and Schumacher: "Traditional Herbal Medicine in Northern Thailand": 1994 edition, White Lotus, Bangkok, Thailand.

[3] Barbara Andaya, "Political Development between the Sixteenth and Eighteenth Centuries" in The Cambridge History of Southeast Asia, Volume One, Part Two, from c.1500 to c.1800 (Singapore: Cambridge University Press, 1992), 66-67.

[4] Anthony Reid, Southeast Asia in the Age of Commerce 1450-1680—Volume Two, Expansion and Crisis (New Haven and London: Yale University Press, 1993), 69.

[5] David Wyatt, Thailand: A Short History (New haven and London: Yale University Press, 1982), 104.

[6] William A. R. Wood, A History of Siam (Bangkok: Chalermnit Bookshop, 1959), 146.

[7] http://www.samurai-archives.com/jia.html

[8] Seiichi Iwao, editor and translator. Jeremias van Vliet Historiael verhael der Sieckte Ende (Tokyo: The Toyo Bunko, 1958) vii-viii.

[9] Kennon Breazeale, "Thai Maritime Trade and the Ministry Responsible" in From Japan to Arabia: Ayutthaya's Maritime Relations with Asia (Bangkok: Printing House of Thammasat University, 1999), 7.

[10] Barbara Andaya, "Political Development between the Sixteenth and Eighteenth Centuries" in The Cambridge History of Southeast Asia, Volume One, Part Two, from c.1500 to c.1800 (Singapore: Cambridge University Press, 1992), 66-67.

[11] Khien Theeravit, "Japanese-Siamese Relations 1606-1629: in Chavit Khamchoo and Reynolds Thai-Japanese Relations in Historical Perspective (Bangkok, Innomedia Co. Ltd., 1988), 19.

[12] Jivaka-Komarabhacca in Pali Cannon: http://www.palikanon.com/english/pali_names/j/jiivaka.htm

[13] Jivaka called "Komarabhaca: "The treatment of infants", VT.ii.174; in Dvy. (506-18)

[14} Jivaka: http://nalanda-insatiableinoffering.blogspot.com/2010/06/jivaka-amravana.html

[15] Jivaka name documented in Pali Cannon: Studies in Traditional Indian Medicine in the Pāli Canon: Jīvaka and Āyurveda", (Kenneth G. Zysk, Journal of the International Association of Buddhist Studies 5, pp. 309–13, 1982)

[16] Jivaka: "Giving of Robes" (Vin.i.268-81; AA.i.216)

[17] Jivaka treats Buddha's ailments: Buddha reads Jivaka's thoughts and bathed as required: Vin.i.279f; DhA. (ii.164f)

[18] Jivaka declared by the Buddha chief among his lay followers loved by the people (aggam puggalappasannānam) (A.i.26)

[19] Jivaka included in a list of good men who have been assured of the realization of deathlessness (A.iii.451; DhΛ.i.244, 247; J.i.116f)

[20] Jivaka and Vejjavatapada: In the seven articles, excerpts from four passages in the Pali canon, the Buddha lays down the attitudes and skills which would make "one who would wait on the sick qualified to nurse the sick." "Doctors Code of Conduct": Anguttara Nikaya III, p.144 (The Vejjavatapada likely predates the Greek Hippocrate Oath.)

[21] Provide for the sick: Brahma Net Sutra, STCUSC, New York, 1998, VI,9.

[22] Traditional Medicine in Kingdom of Thailand: http://www.searo.who.int/entity/medicines/topics/traditional_medicines_in_the_kingdom_of_thailand.pdf?ua=1

[23] Traditional knowledge and traditional medicine: https://www.wto.org/english/tratop_e/trips_e/trilatweb_e/ch2d_trilat_web_13_e.htm

[24] Ministry of Public Health also controls the curricula of the institutions which provides teaching and practicing of Thai traditional medicine.: http://www.thailawforum.com/articles/Thai-traditional-medicine-protection-part1-3.html#64

[25] The efficacies of trance possession ritual performances in contemporary Thai Theravada Buddhism, p. 120: https://ore.exeter.ac.uk/repository/bitstream/handle/10871/15758/ChamchoyP_TPC.pdf?sequence=3&isAllowed=y

[26] The Use of Traditional Medicine in the Thai Health Care System: http://www.thai-institute.net/thai-massage-herbs-articles/Thai%20Healthcare.pdf

[27] The Role of Thai Traditional Medicine in Health Promotion: Vichai Chokevivat, M.D., M.P.H. and Anchalee Chuthaputti, Ph.D. Department for the Development of Thai Traditional and Alternative Medicine, Ministry of Public Health, Thailand

[28] Ban Chiang Archaeological Site: http://whc.unesco.org/en/list/575

[29] Kennon Breazeale, "Thai Maritime Trade and the Ministry Responsible" in From Japan to Arabia: Ayutthaya's Maritime Relations with Asia (Bangkok: Printing House of Thammasat University, 1999), 7.[30] Legal Status of Traditional Medicine and Complimentary/ Alternative Medicine: A Worldwide Review: Thailand: Kennon Breazeale, "Thai Maritime Trade and the Ministry Responsible" in From Japan to Arabia: Ayutthaya's Maritime Relations with Asia (Bangkok: Printing House of Thammasat University, 1999), 7.
[31] Vichi Chockevivat and Anchalee Chuthaputti, 'The Role of Thai Traditional Medicine in Health Promotion' (Paper presented at the 6th Global Conference on Health Promotion, Bangkok, Thailand, 7-11 August 2005) 2.
[32] Angkor influenced Architecture in Thailand: http://www.hellosiam.com/html/Thailand/thailand-history.htm

Additional Resources

Where to gain professional training and certification in ITTM USA

The Thai Yoga Center   www.ThaiYogaCenter.Com

SomaVeda College of Natural Medicine (SCNM)   www.SomaVeda.Org

5401 Saving Grace Ln.
Brooksville, Florida 34602
(706) 358-8646

Where to gain professional training and certification in ITTM in Thailand

www.ThailandStudyTours.Com

Learn more about the science and practice of Indigenous Traditional Thai Medicine and Thai Yoga

www.ThaiMassage.Com

www.FaceBook.Com/LearnThaiYoga

www.YouTube.Com/SomaVeda1

www.BeardedMedia.Com

www.CafePress.com/ThaiMassage

Made in the USA
San Bernardino, CA
17 November 2019

60038753R00040